W0010723

Belongs To:

- - - - - - - - - - - - - - - - - -

Copyright © 2019 Narooma Online Designs
All Rights Reserved

My 28 Day Keto Journey

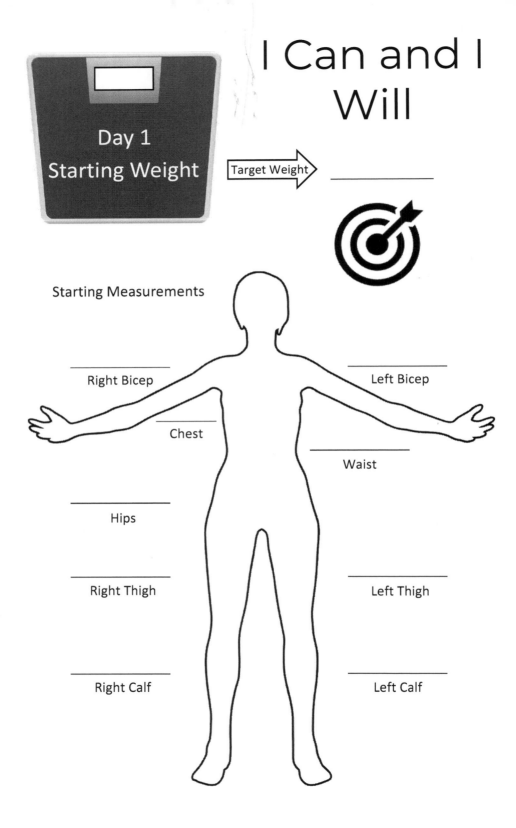

Day 1
Starting Weight

Target Weight _____

I Can and I Will

Starting Measurements

_____ Right Bicep

Chest

_____ Hips

_____ Right Thigh

_____ Right Calf

_____ Left Bicep

_____ Waist

_____ Left Thigh

_____ Left Calf

Before

4"x6"

Questions To Ask Myself

Why am I starting the Keto lifestyle?

_____

_____

_____

_____

What's my end goal?

_____

_____

_____

_____

Do I have a weight loss mindset?

_____

_____

_____

_____

Who can I count on for support?

_____

_____

_____

_____

Day 1 – 7

Meal Planner   Day 1 - 7

Day 1	Breakfast: Lunch: Dinner:
Day 2	Breakfast: Lunch: Dinner:
Day 3	Breakfast: Lunch: Dinner:
Day 4	Breakfast: Lunch: Dinner:
Day 5	Breakfast: Lunch: Dinner:
Day 6	Breakfast: Lunch: Dinner:
Day 7	Breakfast: Lunch: Dinner:
Snacks	

Shopping List   Day 1 - 7

MEAT & FISH	DAIRY	VEGETABLES
Bacon	Heavy Cream	Broccoli
Ground Beef	Full Fat Yogurt	Cauliflower
Chicken	Eggs	Cabbage
Cold Cuts	Butter	Cucumber
Pork	Ghee	Eggplant
Lamb	Sour Cream	Bell Pepper
Organ Meats	Cream Cheese	Asparagus
Duck	Full Fat Cheeses	Salad Mix
Steak	**PANTRY**	Spaghetti Squash
Sausage	Pork Rinds	Zucchini
Shrimp	Almond Milk	Onions
Salmon	Coconut Milk	Garlic
Tuna	Coffee	Celery
FATS & OILS	Himalayan Pink Salt	**FRUITS**
Olive Oil	Mustard	Avocados
Avocado Oil	90% Dark Chocolate	Blueberries
Sesame Oil	Almond Flour	Blackberries
MCT Oil	Coconut Flour	Raspberries
Lard	Bone Broth	Strawberries
Cocoa Butter	Xanthan Gum	Lemons
Coconut Oil	Erythritol	Limes
Nut Butters	Monkfruit	Nuts & Seeds

Shopping List   Day 1 - 7

MEAT & FISH	DAIRY	VEGETABLES
	PANTRY	

FATS & OILS		FRUITS

Habit Tracker

HABIT	1	2	3	4	5	6	7	REWARD

Mood Tracker

DAY	MOOD					WHY?
1	☺	☻	😣	☹	😨	
2	☺	☻	😣	☹	😨	
3	☺	☻	😣	☹	😨	
4	☺	☻	😣	☹	😨	
5	☺	☻	😣	☹	😨	
6	☺	☻	😣	☹	😨	
7	☺	☻	😣	☹	😨	

Only I can change my life!
No one can do it for me.

Exercise Tracker   Day 1 - 7

Day 1	Day 2	Day 3
Cardio ○ Weights ○	Cardio ○ Weights ○	Cardio ○ Weights ○

Day 4	Day 5	Day 6
Cardio ○ Weights ○	Cardio ○ Weights ○	Cardio ○ Weights ○

Day 7	Day	Calories Burned
	1	
	2	
	3	
	4	
	5	
Cardio ○	6	
Weights ○	7	

Food Tracker Day 1   Date: _____

MON TUE WED THU FRI SAT SUN

🎯 Daily Target						
Breakfast	Calories	Fat	Protein	Carbs	Fiber	Net Carbs
Total:						
Lunch	Calories	Fat	Protein	Carbs	Fiber	Net Carbs
Total:						
Dinner	Calories	Fat	Protein	Carbs	Fiber	Net Carbs
Total:						
Snacks	Calories	Fat	Protein	Carbs	Fiber	Net Carbs
Total:						
Daily Total						

Ketosis: Y/N   Intermittent Fasting: From _____am/pm - To_____am/pm

How'd I do?

EAT GOOD
FEEL GOOD

Food Tracker Day 2

Date: _____

MON TUE WED THU FRI SAT SUN

⊕ Daily Target						
Breakfast	Calories	Fat	Protein	Carbs	Fiber	Net Carbs
Total:						
Lunch	Calories	Fat	Protein	Carbs	Fiber	Net Carbs
Total:						
Dinner	Calories	Fat	Protein	Carbs	Fiber	Net Carbs
Total:						
Snacks	Calories	Fat	Protein	Carbs	Fiber	Net Carbs
Total:						
Daily Total						

Ketosis: Y/N   Intermittent Fasting: From _____am/pm - To_____am/pm

How'd I do?

Food Tracker Day 3

Date: _____

MON TUE WED THU FRI SAT SUN

🎯 Daily Target						
Breakfast	Calories	Fat	Protein	Carbs	Fiber	Net Carbs
Total:						
Lunch	Calories	Fat	Protein	Carbs	Fiber	Net Carbs
Total:						
Dinner	Calories	Fat	Protein	Carbs	Fiber	Net Carbs
Total:						
Snacks	Calories	Fat	Protein	Carbs	Fiber	Net Carbs
Total:						
Daily Total						

Ketosis: Y/N   Intermittent Fasting: From _____am/pm - To_____am/pm

How'd I do?

you can do everything

Food Tracker Day 4

Date: _____

MON TUE WED THU FRI SAT SUN

🎯 Daily Target						
Breakfast	Calories	Fat	Protein	Carbs	Fiber	Net Carbs
Total:						
Lunch	Calories	Fat	Protein	Carbs	Fiber	Net Carbs
Total:						
Dinner	Calories	Fat	Protein	Carbs	Fiber	Net Carbs
Total:						
Snacks	Calories	Fat	Protein	Carbs	Fiber	Net Carbs
Total:						
Daily Total						

Ketosis: Y/N   Intermittent Fasting: From _____am/pm - To_____am/pm

How'd I do?

Food Tracker Day 5

Date: _____

🎯 Daily Target						
Breakfast	Calories	Fat	Protein	Carbs	Fiber	Net Carbs
Total:						
Lunch	Calories	Fat	Protein	Carbs	Fiber	Net Carbs
Total:						
Dinner	Calories	Fat	Protein	Carbs	Fiber	Net Carbs
Total:						
Snacks	Calories	Fat	Protein	Carbs	Fiber	Net Carbs
Total:						
Daily Total						

Ketosis: Y/N   Intermittent Fasting: From _____am/pm - To_____am/pm

How'd I do?

BE Stronger THAN YOUR Excuses

Food Tracker Day 6

Date: _____

MON TUE WED THU FRI SAT SUN

⊕ Daily Target						
Breakfast	Calories	Fat	Protein	Carbs	Fiber	Net Carbs
Total:						
Lunch	Calories	Fat	Protein	Carbs	Fiber	Net Carbs
Total:						
Dinner	Calories	Fat	Protein	Carbs	Fiber	Net Carbs
Total:						
Snacks	Calories	Fat	Protein	Carbs	Fiber	Net Carbs
Total:						
Daily Total						

Ketosis: Y/N   Intermittent Fasting: From _____am/pm - To_____am/pm

How'd I do?

Food Tracker Day 7

Date: _____

MON TUE WED THU FRI SAT SUN

⊕ Daily Target						
Breakfast	Calories	Fat	Protein	Carbs	Fiber	Net Carbs
Total:						
Lunch	Calories	Fat	Protein	Carbs	Fiber	Net Carbs
Total:						
Dinner	Calories	Fat	Protein	Carbs	Fiber	Net Carbs
Total:						
Snacks	Calories	Fat	Protein	Carbs	Fiber	Net Carbs
Total:						
Daily Total						

Ketosis: Y/N   Intermittent Fasting: From _____am/pm - To_____am/pm

How'd I do?

When life Gives you
LEMONS
make
LEMONADE!

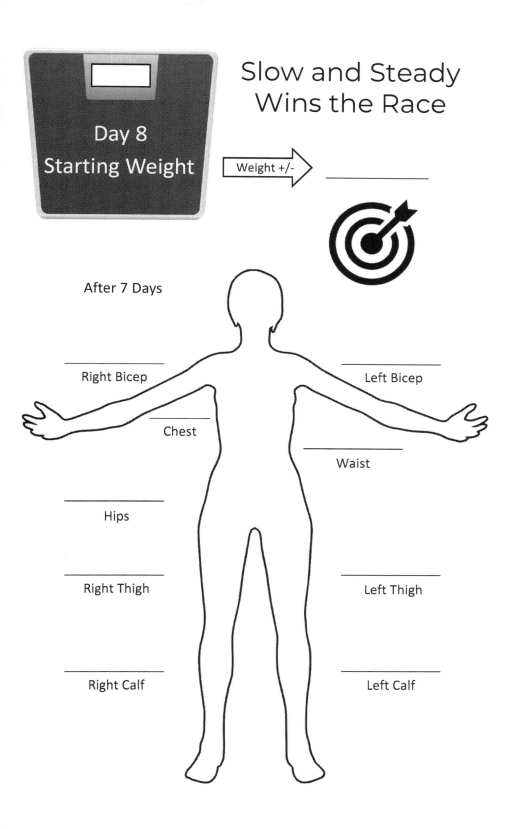

Slow and Steady
Wins the Race

Day 8
Starting Weight

Weight +/- _____

After 7 Days

_____ Right Bicep

Chest _____

_____ Hips

_____ Right Thigh

_____ Right Calf

_____ Left Bicep

Waist _____

_____ Left Thigh

_____ Left Calf

After 7 Days

4"x6"

Questions To Ask Yourself

Am I happy with how I did my first 7 days?

_____

_____

_____

_____

What was my biggest win?

_____

_____

_____

_____

What can I do better at?

_____

_____

_____

_____

How does my body feel?

_____

_____

_____

_____

Day 8 – 14

Meal Planner   Day 8 - 14

Day 8	Breakfast: Lunch: Dinner:
Day 9	Breakfast: Lunch: Dinner:
Day 10	Breakfast: Lunch: Dinner:
Day 11	Breakfast: Lunch: Dinner:
Day 12	Breakfast: Lunch: Dinner:
Day 13	Breakfast: Lunch: Dinner:
Day 14	Breakfast: Lunch: Dinner:
Snacks	

Shopping List   Day 8-14

MEAT & FISH	DAIRY	VEGETABLES
Bacon	Heavy Cream	Broccoli
Ground Beef	Full Fat Yogurt	Cauliflower
Chicken	Eggs	Cabbage
Cold Cuts	Butter	Cucumber
Pork	Ghee	Eggplant
Lamb	Sour Cream	Bell Pepper
Organ Meats	Cream Cheese	Asparagus
Duck	Full Fat Cheeses	Salad Mix
Steak	**PANTRY**	Spaghetti Squash
Sausage	Pork Rinds	Zuchinni
Shrimp	Almond Milk	Onions
Salmon	Coconut Milk	Garlic
Tuna	Coffee	Celery
FATS & OILS	Himalayan Pink Salt	**FRUITS**
Olive Oil	Mustard	Avocados
Avocado Oil	90% Dark Chocolate	Blueberries
Sesame Oil	Almond Flour	Blackberries
MCT Oil	Coconut Flour	Raspberries
Lard	Bone Broth	Strawberries
Cocoa Butter	Xanthan Gum	Lemons
Coconut Oil	Erythritol	Limes
Nut Butters	Monkfruit	Nuts & Seeds

Shopping List   Day 8 - 14

MEAT & FISH	DAIRY	VEGETABLES
	PANTRY	
FATS & OILS		FRUITS

Habit Tracker

HABIT	8	9	10	11	12	13	14	REWARD

Mood Tracker

DAY	MOOD					WHY?
8	☺	☻	😕	☹	😲	
9	☺	☻	😕	☹	😲	
10	☺	☻	😕	☹	😲	
11	☺	☻	😕	☹	😲	
12	☺	☻	😕	☹	😲	
13	☺	☻	😕	☹	😲	
14	☺	☻	😕	☹	😲	

 If you are tired of
starting over
Stop giving up!

Exercise Tracker   Day 8 - 14

Day 8	Day 9	Day 10
Cardio ◯ Weights ◯	Cardio ◯ Weights ◯	Cardio ◯ Weights ◯

Day 11	Day 12	Day 13
Cardio ◯ Weights ◯	Cardio ◯ Weights ◯	Cardio ◯ Weights ◯

Day 14	Day	Calories Burned
	8	
	9	
	10	
	11	
	12	
Cardio ◯	13	
Weights ◯	14	

Food Tracker Day 8

Date: _____

🎯 **Daily Target**						
Breakfast	Calories	Fat	Protein	Carbs	Fiber	Net Carbs
Total:						
Lunch	Calories	Fat	Protein	Carbs	Fiber	Net Carbs
Total:						
Dinner	Calories	Fat	Protein	Carbs	Fiber	Net Carbs
Total:						
Snacks	Calories	Fat	Protein	Carbs	Fiber	Net Carbs
Total:						
Daily Total						

Ketosis: Y/N   Intermittent Fasting: From _____am/pm - To_____am/pm

How'd I do?

Believe **YOU CAN** AND YOU'RE HALFWAY *There*

Theodore Roosevelt

Food Tracker Day 9

Date: _____
MON TUE WED THU FRI SAT SUN

⊕ Daily Target						
Breakfast	Calories	Fat	Protein	Carbs	Fiber	Net Carbs
Total:						
Lunch	Calories	Fat	Protein	Carbs	Fiber	Net Carbs
Total:						
Dinner	Calories	Fat	Protein	Carbs	Fiber	Net Carbs
Total:						
Snacks	Calories	Fat	Protein	Carbs	Fiber	Net Carbs
Total:						
Daily Total						

Ketosis: Y/N   Intermittent Fasting: From _____am/pm - To_____am/pm

How'd I do?

Food Tracker Day 10

Date: _____

MON TUE WED THU FRI SAT SUN

🎯 Daily Target						
Breakfast	Calories	Fat	Protein	Carbs	Fiber	Net Carbs
Total:						
Lunch	Calories	Fat	Protein	Carbs	Fiber	Net Carbs
Total:						
Dinner	Calories	Fat	Protein	Carbs	Fiber	Net Carbs
Total:						
Snacks	Calories	Fat	Protein	Carbs	Fiber	Net Carbs
Total:						
Daily Total						

Ketosis: Y/N   Intermittent Fasting: From _____am/pm - To_____am/pm

How'd I do?

THE distance BEETWEN your DREAMS AND reality is called ACTION.

Food Tracker Day 11

🎯 Daily Target						
Breakfast	Calories	Fat	Protein	Carbs	Fiber	Net Carbs
Total:						
Lunch	Calories	Fat	Protein	Carbs	Fiber	Net Carbs
Total:						
Dinner	Calories	Fat	Protein	Carbs	Fiber	Net Carbs
Total:						
Snacks	Calories	Fat	Protein	Carbs	Fiber	Net Carbs
Total:						
Daily Total						

Ketosis: Y/N   Intermittent Fasting: From _____am/pm - To_____am/pm

How'd I do?

Food Tracker Day 12

Date: _____

MON TUE WED THU FRI SAT SUN

⊕ Daily Target						
Breakfast	Calories	Fat	Protein	Carbs	Fiber	Net Carbs
Total:						
Lunch	Calories	Fat	Protein	Carbs	Fiber	Net Carbs
Total:						
Dinner	Calories	Fat	Protein	Carbs	Fiber	Net Carbs
Total:						
Snacks	Calories	Fat	Protein	Carbs	Fiber	Net Carbs
Total:						
Daily Total						

Ketosis: Y/N   Intermittent Fasting: From _____am/pm - To_____am/pm

How'd I do?

TOMORROW is a new day

Food Tracker Day 13

Date: _____

MON TUE WED THU FRI SAT SUN

⊕ **Daily Target**						
Breakfast	Calories	Fat	Protein	Carbs	Fiber	Net Carbs
Total:						
Lunch	Calories	Fat	Protein	Carbs	Fiber	Net Carbs
Total:						
Dinner	Calories	Fat	Protein	Carbs	Fiber	Net Carbs
Total:						
Snacks	Calories	Fat	Protein	Carbs	Fiber	Net Carbs
Total:						
Daily Total						

Ketosis: Y/N   Intermittent Fasting: From _____am/pm - To_____am/pm

How'd I do?

Food Tracker Day 14

Date: _____

⌖ Daily Target						
Breakfast	Calories	Fat	Protein	Carbs	Fiber	Net Carbs
Total:						
Lunch	Calories	Fat	Protein	Carbs	Fiber	Net Carbs
Total:						
Dinner	Calories	Fat	Protein	Carbs	Fiber	Net Carbs
Total:						
Snacks	Calories	Fat	Protein	Carbs	Fiber	Net Carbs
Total:						
Daily Total						

Ketosis: Y/N   Intermittent Fasting: From _____am/pm - To_____am/pm

How'd I do?

.DON'T.
Quit
Just
DO·IT

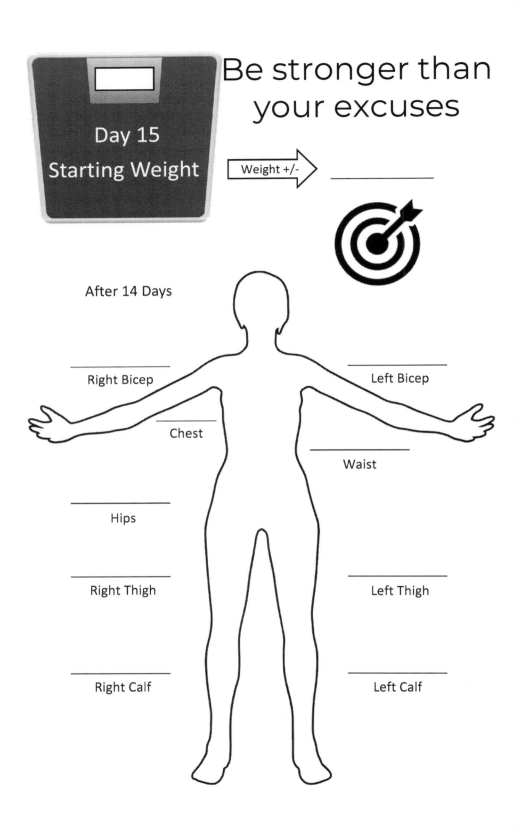

Day 15
Starting Weight

Be stronger than your excuses

Weight +/- _____

After 14 Days

_____
Right Bicep

_____
Left Bicep

_____
Chest

_____
Waist

_____
Hips

_____
Right Thigh

_____
Left Thigh

_____
Right Calf

_____
Left Calf

After 14 Days

4"x6"

Questions To Ask Yourself

Is it getting easier or harder to stick to Keto? Why?

_____

_____

_____

_____

What's my biggest issue with eating the Keto way?

_____

_____

_____

_____

Is there anything I can do to make it easier?

_____

_____

_____

_____

What is the food I miss most? Is there a Keto substitute for it?

_____

_____

_____

_____

Day 15 – 21

Meal Planner   Day 15 - 21

Day 15	Breakfast: Lunch: Dinner:
Day 16	Breakfast: Lunch: Dinner:
Day 17	Breakfast: Lunch: Dinner:
Day 18	Breakfast: Lunch: Dinner:
Day 19	Breakfast: Lunch: Dinner:
Day 20	Breakfast: Lunch: Dinner:
Day 21	Breakfast: Lunch: Dinner:
Snacks	

Shopping List — Day 15 - 21

MEAT & FISH		DAIRY		VEGETABLES	
	Bacon		Heavy Cream		Broccoli
	Ground Beef		Full Fat Yogurt		Cauliflower
	Chicken		Eggs		Cabbage
	Cold Cuts		Butter		Cucumber
	Pork		Ghee		Eggplant
	Lamb		Sour Cream		Bell Pepper
	Organ Meats		Cream Cheese		Asparagus
	Duck		Full Fat Cheeses		Salad Mix
	Steak	**PANTRY**			Spaghetti Squash
	Sausage		Pork Rinds		Zucchini
	Shrimp		Almond Milk		Onions
	Salmon		Coconut Milk		Garlic
	Tuna		Coffee		Celery
FATS & OILS			Himalayan Pink Salt	**FRUITS**	
	Olive Oil		Mustard		Avocados
	Avocado Oil		90% Dark Chocolate		Blueberries
	Sesame Oil		Almond Flour		Blackberries
	MCT Oil		Coconut Flour		Raspberries
	Lard		Bone Broth		Strawberries
	Cocoa Butter		Xanthan Gum		Lemons
	Coconut Oil		Erythritol		Limes
	Nut Butters		Monkfruit		Nuts & Seeds

Shopping List   Day 15 -21

MEAT & FISH	DAIRY	VEGETABLES
	PANTRY	
FATS & OILS		FRUITS

Habit Tracker

HABIT	15	16	17	18	19	20	21	REWARD

Mood Tracker

DAY	MOOD					WHY?
15	☺	☺	☹	☹	☹	
16	☺	☺	☹	☹	☹	
17	☺	☺	☹	☹	☹	
18	☺	☺	☹	☹	☹	
19	☺	☺	☹	☹	☹	
20	☺	☺	☹	☹	☹	
21	☺	☺	☹	☹	☹	

 One pound at a time!

Exercise Tracker   Day 15 - 21

Day 15	Day 16	Day 17
Cardio ○ Weights ○	Cardio ○ Weights ○	Cardio ○ Weights ○

Day 18	Day 19	Day 20
Cardio ○ Weights ○	Cardio ○ Weights ○	Cardio ○ Weights ○

Day 21
Cardio ○ Weights ○

Day	Calories Burned
15	
16	
17	
18	
19	
20	
21	

Food Tracker Day 15

Date: _____

MON TUE WED THU FRI SAT SUN

⊕ Daily Target						
Breakfast	Calories	Fat	Protein	Carbs	Fiber	Net Carbs
Total:						
Lunch	Calories	Fat	Protein	Carbs	Fiber	Net Carbs
Total:						
Dinner	Calories	Fat	Protein	Carbs	Fiber	Net Carbs
Total:						
Snacks	Calories	Fat	Protein	Carbs	Fiber	Net Carbs
Total:						
Daily Total						

Ketosis: Y/N   Intermittent Fasting: From _____am/pm - To_____am/pm

How'd I do?

Food Tracker Day 16

Date: _____

🎯 Daily Target						
Breakfast	Calories	Fat	Protein	Carbs	Fiber	Net Carbs
Total:						
Lunch	Calories	Fat	Protein	Carbs	Fiber	Net Carbs
Total:						
Dinner	Calories	Fat	Protein	Carbs	Fiber	Net Carbs
Total:						
Snacks	Calories	Fat	Protein	Carbs	Fiber	Net Carbs
Total:						
Daily Total						

Ketosis: Y/N   Intermittent Fasting: From _____am/pm - To_____am/pm

How'd I do?

All
THINGS
ARE
possible

Food Tracker Day 17

Date: _____

MON TUE WED THU FRI SAT SUN

🎯 Daily Target						

Breakfast	Calories	Fat	Protein	Carbs	Fiber	Net Carbs
Total:						

Lunch	Calories	Fat	Protein	Carbs	Fiber	Net Carbs
Total:						

Dinner	Calories	Fat	Protein	Carbs	Fiber	Net Carbs
Total:						

Snacks	Calories	Fat	Protein	Carbs	Fiber	Net Carbs
Total:						

Daily Total						

Ketosis: Y/N   Intermittent Fasting: From _____am/pm - To_____am/pm

How'd I do?

Food Tracker Day 18

Date: _____

🎯 Daily Target						
Breakfast	Calories	Fat	Protein	Carbs	Fiber	Net Carbs
Total:						
Lunch	Calories	Fat	Protein	Carbs	Fiber	Net Carbs
Total:						
Dinner	Calories	Fat	Protein	Carbs	Fiber	Net Carbs
Total:						
Snacks	Calories	Fat	Protein	Carbs	Fiber	Net Carbs
Total:						
Daily Total						

Ketosis: Y/N   Intermittent Fasting: From _____am/pm - To_____am/pm

How'd I do?

_____

_____

_____

_____

_____

_____

_____

_____

_____

_____

_____

_____

_____

_____

_____

_____

_____

_____

_____

6 MONTHS FROM NOW
you're not going to remember
how those cookies tasted,
but you will able
to see results.

Food Tracker Day 19

Date: _____

MON TUE WED THU FRI SAT SUN

⊕ Daily Target						
Breakfast	Calories	Fat	Protein	Carbs	Fiber	Net Carbs
Total:						
Lunch	Calories	Fat	Protein	Carbs	Fiber	Net Carbs
Total:						
Dinner	Calories	Fat	Protein	Carbs	Fiber	Net Carbs
Total:						
Snacks	Calories	Fat	Protein	Carbs	Fiber	Net Carbs
Total:						
Daily Total						

Ketosis: Y/N   Intermittent Fasting: From _____am/pm - To_____am/pm

How'd I do?

Food Tracker Day 20

Date: _____

MON TUE WED THU FRI SAT SUN

⊕ Daily Target						
Breakfast	Calories	Fat	Protein	Carbs	Fiber	Net Carbs
Total:						
Lunch	Calories	Fat	Protein	Carbs	Fiber	Net Carbs
Total:						
Dinner	Calories	Fat	Protein	Carbs	Fiber	Net Carbs
Total:						
Snacks	Calories	Fat	Protein	Carbs	Fiber	Net Carbs
Total:						
Daily Total						

Ketosis: Y/N   Intermittent Fasting: From _____am/pm - To_____am/pm

How'd I do?

DO NOT
EAT LESS
EAT
RIGHT

Food Tracker Day 21

Date: _____

MON TUE WED THU FRI SAT SUN

🎯 Daily Target						
Breakfast	Calories	Fat	Protein	Carbs	Fiber	Net Carbs
Total:						
Lunch	Calories	Fat	Protein	Carbs	Fiber	Net Carbs
Total:						
Dinner	Calories	Fat	Protein	Carbs	Fiber	Net Carbs
Total:						
Snacks	Calories	Fat	Protein	Carbs	Fiber	Net Carbs
Total:						
Daily Total						

Ketosis: Y/N   Intermittent Fasting: From _____am/pm - To_____am/pm

How'd I do?

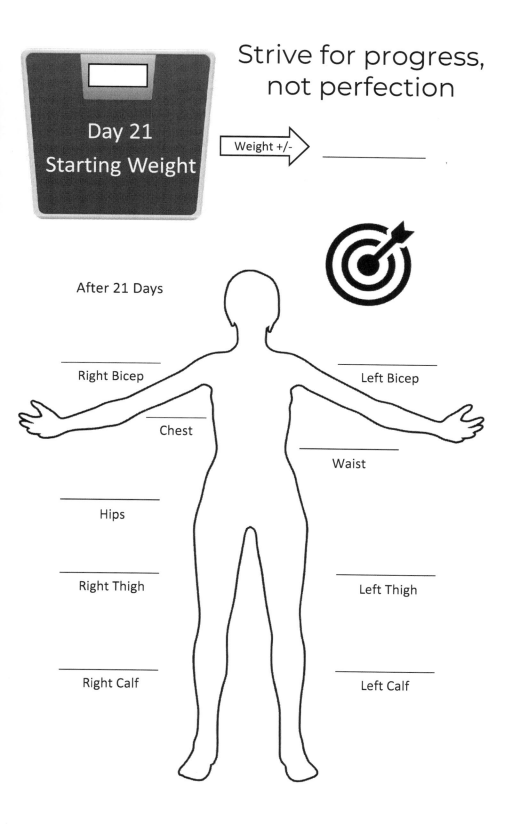

Strive for progress, not perfection

Day 21
Starting Weight

Weight +/- _____

After 21 Days

_____ Right Bicep

_____ Left Bicep

_____ Chest

_____ Waist

_____ Hips

_____ Right Thigh

_____ Left Thigh

_____ Right Calf

_____ Left Calf

After 21 Days

4"x6"

Questions To Ask Yourself

Will I continue with this way of eating? Why or why not?

_____

_____

_____

_____

Can I do this alone or do I need more support?

_____

_____

_____

_____

Even if I reach my goal I will stick to Keto. True or False?

_____

_____

_____

_____

I would recommend the Keto lifestyle to friends & family?

_____

_____

_____

_____

Day 22-28

Meal Planner   Day 22 - 28

Day 22	Breakfast: Lunch: Dinner:
Day 23	Breakfast: Lunch: Dinner:
Day 24	Breakfast: Lunch: Dinner:
Day 25	Breakfast: Lunch: Dinner:
Day 26	Breakfast: Lunch: Dinner:
Day 27	Breakfast: Lunch: Dinner:
Day 28	Breakfast: Lunch: Dinner:
Snacks	

Shopping List   Day 22 - 28

MEAT & FISH	DAIRY	VEGETABLES
Bacon	Heavy Cream	Broccoli
Ground Beef	Full Fat Yogurt	Cauliflower
Chicken	Eggs	Cabbage
Cold Cuts	Butter	Cucumber
Pork	Ghee	Eggplant
Lamb	Sour Cream	Bell Pepper
Organ Meats	Cream Cheese	Asparagus
Duck	Full Fat Cheeses	Salad Mix
Steak	**PANTRY**	Spaghetti Squash
Sausage	Pork Rinds	Zucchini
Shrimp	Almond Milk	Onions
Salmon	Coconut Milk	Garlic
Tuna	Coffee	Celery
FATS & OILS	Himalayan Pink Salt	**FRUITS**
Olive Oil	Mustard	Avocados
Avocado Oil	90% Dark Chocolate	Blueberries
Sesame Oil	Almond Flour	Blackberries
MCT Oil	Coconut Flour	Raspberries
Lard	Bone Broth	Strawberries
Cocoa Butter	Xanthan Gum	Lemons
Coconut Oil	Erythritol	Limes
Nut Butters	Monkfruit	Nuts & Seeds

Shopping List   Day 22 -28

MEAT & FISH		DAIRY		VEGETABLES
		PANTRY		
FATS & OILS				**FRUITS**

Habit Tracker

HABIT	22	23	24	25	26	27	28	REWARD

Mood Tracker

DAY	MOOD					WHY?
22	☺	☻	☹	☹	☹	
23	☺	☻	☹	☹	☹	
24	☺	☻	☹	☹	☹	
25	☺	☻	☹	☹	☹	
26	☺	☻	☹	☹	☹	
27	☺	☻	☹	☹	☹	
28	☺	☻	☹	☹	☹	

 One pound at a time!

Exercise Tracker   Day 22 - 28

Day 22	Day 23	Day 24
Cardio ○ Weights ○	Cardio ○ Weights ○	Cardio ○ Weights ○

Day 25	Day 26	Day 27
Cardio ○ Weights ○	Cardio ○ Weights ○	Cardio ○ Weights ○

Day 28		Day	Calories Burned
		22	
		23	
		24	
		25	
		26	
Cardio ○		27	
Weights ○		28	

Food Tracker Day 22

Date: _____
MON TUE WED THU FRI SAT SUN

⊕ Daily Target						
Breakfast	Calories	Fat	Protein	Carbs	Fiber	Net Carbs
Total:						
Lunch	Calories	Fat	Protein	Carbs	Fiber	Net Carbs
Total:						
Dinner	Calories	Fat	Protein	Carbs	Fiber	Net Carbs
Total:						
Snacks	Calories	Fat	Protein	Carbs	Fiber	Net Carbs
Total:						
Daily Total						

Ketosis: Y/N   Intermittent Fasting: From _____am/pm - To_____am/pm

How'd I do?

MY cooking IS SO FABULOUS
EVEN THE SMOKE ALARM
CHEERS ME ON

Food Tracker Day 23

Date: _____

MON TUE WED THU FRI SAT SUN

🎯 Daily Target						
Breakfast	Calories	Fat	Protein	Carbs	Fiber	Net Carbs
Total:						
Lunch	Calories	Fat	Protein	Carbs	Fiber	Net Carbs
Total:						
Dinner	Calories	Fat	Protein	Carbs	Fiber	Net Carbs
Total:						
Snacks	Calories	Fat	Protein	Carbs	Fiber	Net Carbs
Total:						
Daily Total						

Ketosis: Y/N   Intermittent Fasting: From _____am/pm - To_____am/pm

How'd I do?

Food Tracker Day 24

Date: _____

MON TUE WED THU FRI SAT SUN

⊕ Daily Target						
Breakfast	Calories	Fat	Protein	Carbs	Fiber	Net Carbs
Total:						
Lunch	Calories	Fat	Protein	Carbs	Fiber	Net Carbs
Total:						
Dinner	Calories	Fat	Protein	Carbs	Fiber	Net Carbs
Total:						
Snacks	Calories	Fat	Protein	Carbs	Fiber	Net Carbs
Total:						
Daily Total						

Ketosis: Y/N   Intermittent Fasting: From _____am/pm - To_____am/pm

How'd I do?

GOOD
FOOD
IS
GOOD
MOOD

Food Tracker Day 25

🎯 **Daily Target**						
Breakfast	Calories	Fat	Protein	Carbs	Fiber	Net Carbs
Total:						
Lunch	Calories	Fat	Protein	Carbs	Fiber	Net Carbs
Total:						
Dinner	Calories	Fat	Protein	Carbs	Fiber	Net Carbs
Total:						
Snacks	Calories	Fat	Protein	Carbs	Fiber	Net Carbs
Total:						
Daily Total						

Ketosis: Y/N   Intermittent Fasting: From _____am/pm - To_____am/pm

How'd I do?

Food Tracker Day 26

Date: _____

🎯 Daily Target						
Breakfast	Calories	Fat	Protein	Carbs	Fiber	Net Carbs
Total:						
Lunch	Calories	Fat	Protein	Carbs	Fiber	Net Carbs
Total:						
Dinner	Calories	Fat	Protein	Carbs	Fiber	Net Carbs
Total:						
Snacks	Calories	Fat	Protein	Carbs	Fiber	Net Carbs
Total:						
Daily Total						

Ketosis: Y/N   Intermittent Fasting: From _____am/pm - To_____am/pm

How'd I do?

Food Tracker Day 27

🎯 Daily Target						
Breakfast	Calories	Fat	Protein	Carbs	Fiber	Net Carbs
Total:						
Lunch	Calories	Fat	Protein	Carbs	Fiber	Net Carbs
Total:						
Dinner	Calories	Fat	Protein	Carbs	Fiber	Net Carbs
Total:						
Snacks	Calories	Fat	Protein	Carbs	Fiber	Net Carbs
Total:						
Daily Total						

Ketosis: Y/N   Intermittent Fasting: From _____am/pm - To_____am/pm

How'd I do?

Food Tracker Day 28

⊕ Daily Target						
Breakfast	Calories	Fat	Protein	Carbs	Fiber	Net Carbs
Total:						
Lunch	Calories	Fat	Protein	Carbs	Fiber	Net Carbs
Total:						
Dinner	Calories	Fat	Protein	Carbs	Fiber	Net Carbs
Total:						
Snacks	Calories	Fat	Protein	Carbs	Fiber	Net Carbs
Total:						
Daily Total						

Ketosis: Y/N   Intermittent Fasting: From _____am/pm - To_____am/pm

How'd I do?

YOU DON'T Have To Be PERFECT TO BE Amazing

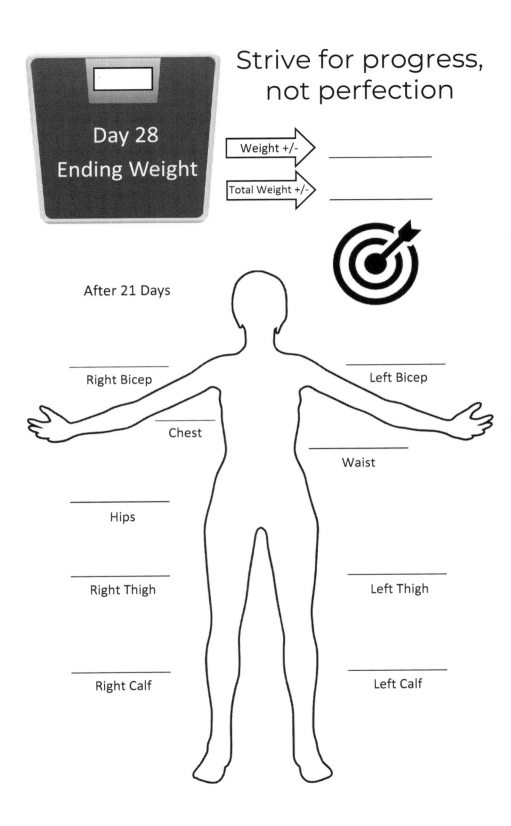

Strive for progress, not perfection

Day 28
Ending Weight

Weight +/- _____

Total Weight +/- _____

After 21 Days

_____
Right Bicep

_____
Left Bicep

_____
Chest

_____
Waist

_____
Hips

_____
Right Thigh

_____
Left Thigh

_____
Right Calf

_____
Left Calf

After 28 Days

4"x6"

Questions To Ask Yourself

Will I continue with this way of eating? Why or why not?

_____

_____

_____

_____

Can I do this alone or do I need more support?

_____

_____

_____

_____

Even if I reach my goal I will stick to Keto. True or False?

_____

_____

_____

_____

I would recommend the Keto lifestyle to friends & family?

_____

_____

_____

_____

"don't trust
what you see
even salt
looks like
sugar"

Keto
Recipes

Recipe: _____

Prep Time [   ] Cook Time [   ] Servings [   ] Difficulty [   ]

Ingredients

_____

_____

_____

_____

_____

_____

Directions

_____

_____

_____

_____

_____

_____

_____

_____

_____

_____

_____

_____

Protein [   ] Fat [   ] Carbs [   ] Fiber [   ] Calories [   ]

Recipe: ───────────────

Prep Time [   ] Cook Time [   ] Servings [   ] Difficulty [   ]

Ingredients

_____

_____

_____

_____

_____

_____

Directions

_____

_____

_____

_____

_____

_____

_____

_____

_____

Protein [   ] Fat [   ] Carbs [   ] Fiber [   ] Calories [   ]

Recipe: _____

Prep Time [   ]   Cook Time [   ]   Servings [   ]   Difficulty [   ]

Ingredients

_____

_____

_____

_____

_____

_____

_____

Directions

_____

_____

_____

_____

_____

_____

_____

_____

_____

_____

_____

_____

Protein [   ]   Fat [   ]   Carbs [   ]   Fiber [   ]   Calories [   ]

Recipe: ───────────────────

Prep Time [   ] Cook Time [   ] Servings [   ] Difficulty [   ]

Ingredients

_____

_____

_____

_____

_____

_____

_____

Directions

_____

_____

_____

_____

_____

_____

_____

_____

_____

_____

_____

Protein [   ] Fat [   ] Carbs [   ] Fiber [   ] Calories [   ]

Recipe: _____

Prep Time [   ] Cook Time [   ] Servings [   ] Difficulty [   ]

Ingredients

_____

_____

_____

_____

_____

_____

Directions

_____

_____

_____

_____

_____

_____

_____

_____

_____

_____

_____

Protein [   ] Fat [   ] Carbs [   ] Fiber [   ] Calories [   ]

Recipe: ———————————

Prep Time [   ] Cook Time [   ] Servings [   ] Difficulty [   ]

Ingredients

_____

_____

_____

_____

_____

_____

Directions

_____

_____

_____

_____

_____

_____

_____

_____

_____

_____

Protein [   ] Fat [   ] Carbs [   ] Fiber [   ] Calories [   ]

Recipe: _____

Prep Time [   ] Cook Time [   ] Servings [   ] Difficulty [   ]

Ingredients

_____

_____

_____

_____

_____

_____

Directions

_____

_____

_____

_____

_____

_____

_____

_____

_____

_____

_____

Protein [   ] Fat [   ] Carbs [   ] Fiber [   ] Calories [   ]

Recipe: ————————————

Prep Time [   ] Cook Time [   ] Servings [   ] Difficulty [   ]

Ingredients

_____

_____

_____

_____

_____

_____

Directions

_____

_____

_____

_____

_____

_____

_____

_____

_____

_____

Protein [   ] Fat [   ] Carbs [   ] Fiber [   ] Calories [   ]

Recipe: _____

Prep Time [   ] Cook Time [   ] Servings [   ] Difficulty [   ]

Ingredients

_____

_____

_____

_____

_____

_____

_____

Directions

_____

_____

_____

_____

_____

_____

_____

_____

_____

_____

_____

Protein [   ] Fat [   ] Carbs [   ] Fiber [   ] Calories [   ]

Recipe: _____

Prep Time [   ] Cook Time [   ] Servings [   ] Difficulty [   ]

Ingredients

_____

_____

_____

_____

_____

_____

Directions

_____

_____

_____

_____

_____

_____

_____

_____

_____

Protein [   ] Fat [   ] Carbs [   ] Fiber [   ] Calories [   ]

Recipe: _____

Prep Time [   ] Cook Time [   ] Servings [   ] Difficulty [   ]

Ingredients

_____

_____

_____

_____

_____

_____

_____

Directions

_____

_____

_____

_____

_____

_____

_____

_____

_____

_____

_____

Protein [   ] Fat [   ] Carbs [   ] Fiber [   ] Calories [   ]

Recipe: _____

Prep Time [   ] Cook Time [   ] Servings [   ] Difficulty [   ]

Ingredients

_____

_____

_____

_____

_____

_____

_____

Directions

_____

_____

_____

_____

_____

_____

_____

_____

_____

_____

_____

Protein [   ] Fat [   ] Carbs [   ] Fiber [   ] Calories [   ]

Recipe: _____

Prep Time [　　] Cook Time [　　] Servings [　　] Difficulty [　　]

Ingredients

_____

_____

_____

_____

_____

_____

Directions

_____

_____

_____

_____

_____

_____

_____

_____

_____

_____

_____

Protein [　　] Fat [　　] Carbs [　　] Fiber [　　] Calories [　　]

Recipe: ──────────────

Prep Time [   ] Cook Time [   ] Servings [   ] Difficulty [   ]

Ingredients

_____

_____

_____

_____

_____

_____

_____

Directions

_____

_____

_____

_____

_____

_____

_____

_____

_____

_____

_____

Protein [   ] Fat [   ] Carbs [   ] Fiber [   ] Calories [   ]

Recipe: _____

Prep Time [   ] Cook Time [   ] Servings [   ] Difficulty [   ]

Ingredients

_____

_____

_____

_____

_____

_____

Directions

_____

_____

_____

_____

_____

_____

_____

_____

_____

_____

_____

Protein [   ] Fat [   ] Carbs [   ] Fiber [   ] Calories [   ]

Recipe: ───────────────

Prep Time [   ] Cook Time [   ] Servings [   ] Difficulty [   ]

Ingredients

_____

_____

_____

_____

_____

_____

Directions

_____

_____

_____

_____

_____

_____

_____

_____

_____

_____

Protein [   ] Fat [   ] Carbs [   ] Fiber [   ] Calories [   ]

Recipe: ─────────────

Prep Time [   ] Cook Time [   ] Servings [   ] Difficulty [   ]

Ingredients

_____

_____

_____

_____

_____

_____

Directions

_____

_____

_____

_____

_____

_____

_____

_____

_____

_____

_____

Protein [   ] Fat [   ] Carbs [   ] Fiber [   ] Calories [   ]

Recipe: ——————————————

Prep Time [   ] Cook Time [   ] Servings [   ] Difficulty [   ]

Ingredients

_____

_____

_____

_____

_____

_____

_____

Directions

_____

_____

_____

_____

_____

_____

_____

_____

_____

_____

Protein [   ] Fat [   ] Carbs [   ] Fiber [   ] Calories [   ]

Recipe: _____

Prep Time [   ] Cook Time [   ] Servings [   ] Difficulty [   ]

Ingredients

_____

_____

_____

_____

_____

_____

Directions

_____

_____

_____

_____

_____

_____

_____

_____

_____

_____

Protein [   ] Fat [   ] Carbs [   ] Fiber [   ] Calories [   ]

Recipe: ───────────────

Prep Time [   ] Cook Time [   ] Servings [   ] Difficulty [   ]

Ingredients

_____

_____

_____

_____

_____

_____

_____

Directions

_____

_____

_____

_____

_____

_____

_____

_____

_____

_____

Protein [   ] Fat [   ] Carbs [   ] Fiber [   ] Calories [   ]

Recipe: _____

Prep Time [   ] Cook Time [   ] Servings [   ] Difficulty [   ]

Ingredients

_____

_____

_____

_____

_____

_____

_____

Directions

_____

_____

_____

_____

_____

_____

_____

_____

_____

_____

_____

_____

Protein [   ] Fat [   ] Carbs [   ] Fiber [   ] Calories [   ]

Recipe: _____

Prep Time [   ] Cook Time [   ] Servings [   ] Difficulty [   ]

Ingredients

_____

_____

_____

_____

_____

_____

Directions

_____

_____

_____

_____

_____

_____

_____

_____

_____

_____

Protein [   ] Fat [   ] Carbs [   ] Fiber [   ] Calories [   ]

Recipe: _____

Prep Time [   ] Cook Time [   ] Servings [   ] Difficulty [   ]

Ingredients

_____

_____

_____

_____

_____

_____

Directions

_____

_____

_____

_____

_____

_____

_____

_____

_____

_____

_____

Protein [   ] Fat [   ] Carbs [   ] Fiber [   ] Calories [   ]

Recipe: _____

Prep Time [   ]   Cook Time [   ]   Servings [   ]   Difficulty [   ]

Ingredients

_____

_____

_____

_____

_____

_____

Directions

_____

_____

_____

_____

_____

_____

_____

_____

_____

_____

Protein [   ]   Fat [   ]   Carbs [   ]   Fiber [   ]   Calories [   ]

Recipe: _____

Prep Time [　　] Cook Time [　　] Servings [　　] Difficulty [　　]

Ingredients

_____

_____

_____

_____

_____

_____

Directions

_____

_____

_____

_____

_____

_____

_____

_____

_____

_____

_____

Protein [　　] Fat [　　] Carbs [　　] Fiber [　　] Calories [　　]

Recipe: _____

Prep Time [   ] Cook Time [   ] Servings [   ] Difficulty [   ]

Ingredients

_____

_____

_____

_____

_____

_____

Directions

_____

_____

_____

_____

_____

_____

_____

_____

_____

_____

Protein [   ] Fat [   ] Carbs [   ] Fiber [   ] Calories [   ]

Recipe: _____

Prep Time [   ] Cook Time [   ] Servings [   ] Difficulty [   ]

Ingredients

_____

_____

_____

_____

_____

_____

Directions

_____

_____

_____

_____

_____

_____

_____

_____

_____

_____

Protein [   ] Fat [   ] Carbs [   ] Fiber [   ] Calories [   ]

Recipe: ───────────

Prep Time [   ] Cook Time [   ] Servings [   ] Difficulty [   ]

Ingredients

_____

_____

_____

_____

_____

_____

_____

Directions

_____

_____

_____

_____

_____

_____

_____

_____

_____

_____

Protein [   ] Fat [   ] Carbs [   ] Fiber [   ] Calories [   ]

Recipe: _____

Prep Time [   ] Cook Time [   ] Servings [   ] Difficulty [   ]

Ingredients

_____

_____

_____

_____

_____

_____

Directions

_____

_____

_____

_____

_____

_____

_____

_____

_____

_____

_____

Protein [   ] Fat [   ] Carbs [   ] Fiber [   ] Calories [   ]

Recipe: ———————————————

Prep Time [   ] Cook Time [   ] Servings [   ] Difficulty [   ]

Ingredients

_____

_____

_____

_____

_____

_____

Directions

_____

_____

_____

_____

_____

_____

_____

_____

_____

_____

Protein [   ] Fat [   ] Carbs [   ] Fiber [   ] Calories [   ]

Recipe: _____

Prep Time [   ] Cook Time [   ] Servings [   ] Difficulty [   ]

Ingredients

_____

_____

_____

_____

_____

_____

Directions

_____

_____

_____

_____

_____

_____

_____

_____

_____

_____

_____

_____

Protein [   ] Fat [   ] Carbs [   ] Fiber [   ] Calories [   ]

Recipe: ───────────────

Prep Time [　　] Cook Time [　　] Servings [　　] Difficulty [　　]

Ingredients

_____

_____

_____

_____

_____

_____

_____

Directions

_____

_____

_____

_____

_____

_____

_____

_____

_____

_____

_____

Protein [　　] Fat [　　] Carbs [　　] Fiber [　　] Calories [　　]

Recipe: _____

Prep Time [   ] Cook Time [   ] Servings [   ] Difficulty [   ]

Ingredients

_____

_____

_____

_____

_____

_____

_____

Directions

_____

_____

_____

_____

_____

_____

_____

_____

_____

_____

_____

_____

Protein [   ] Fat [   ] Carbs [   ] Fiber [   ] Calories [   ]

Recipe: _____

Prep Time [   ] Cook Time [   ] Servings [   ] Difficulty [   ]

Ingredients

_____

_____

_____

_____

_____

_____

_____

Directions

_____

_____

_____

_____

_____

_____

_____

_____

_____

_____

Protein [   ] Fat [   ] Carbs [   ] Fiber [   ] Calories [   ]

Recipe: _____

Prep Time [   ] Cook Time [   ] Servings [   ] Difficulty [   ]

Ingredients

_____

_____

_____

_____

_____

_____

_____

Directions

_____

_____

_____

_____

_____

_____

_____

_____

_____

_____

_____

Protein [   ] Fat [   ] Carbs [   ] Fiber [   ] Calories [   ]

Recipe: ⎯⎯⎯⎯⎯⎯⎯⎯⎯⎯

Prep Time [　　] Cook Time [　　] Servings [　　] Difficulty [　　]

Ingredients

⎯⎯⎯⎯⎯⎯⎯⎯⎯⎯⎯⎯⎯⎯⎯⎯⎯⎯⎯⎯⎯⎯⎯⎯⎯⎯⎯⎯⎯⎯⎯⎯⎯⎯

⎯⎯⎯⎯⎯⎯⎯⎯⎯⎯⎯⎯⎯⎯⎯⎯⎯⎯⎯⎯⎯⎯⎯⎯⎯⎯⎯⎯⎯⎯⎯⎯⎯⎯

⎯⎯⎯⎯⎯⎯⎯⎯⎯⎯⎯⎯⎯⎯⎯⎯⎯⎯⎯⎯⎯⎯⎯⎯⎯⎯⎯⎯⎯⎯⎯⎯⎯⎯

⎯⎯⎯⎯⎯⎯⎯⎯⎯⎯⎯⎯⎯⎯⎯⎯⎯⎯⎯⎯⎯⎯⎯⎯⎯⎯⎯⎯⎯⎯⎯⎯⎯⎯

⎯⎯⎯⎯⎯⎯⎯⎯⎯⎯⎯⎯⎯⎯⎯⎯⎯⎯⎯⎯⎯⎯⎯⎯⎯⎯⎯⎯⎯⎯⎯⎯⎯⎯

⎯⎯⎯⎯⎯⎯⎯⎯⎯⎯⎯⎯⎯⎯⎯⎯⎯⎯⎯⎯⎯⎯⎯⎯⎯⎯⎯⎯⎯⎯⎯⎯⎯⎯

Directions

⎯⎯⎯⎯⎯⎯⎯⎯⎯⎯⎯⎯⎯⎯⎯⎯⎯⎯⎯⎯⎯⎯⎯⎯⎯⎯⎯⎯⎯⎯⎯⎯⎯⎯

⎯⎯⎯⎯⎯⎯⎯⎯⎯⎯⎯⎯⎯⎯⎯⎯⎯⎯⎯⎯⎯⎯⎯⎯⎯⎯⎯⎯⎯⎯⎯⎯⎯⎯

⎯⎯⎯⎯⎯⎯⎯⎯⎯⎯⎯⎯⎯⎯⎯⎯⎯⎯⎯⎯⎯⎯⎯⎯⎯⎯⎯⎯⎯⎯⎯⎯⎯⎯

⎯⎯⎯⎯⎯⎯⎯⎯⎯⎯⎯⎯⎯⎯⎯⎯⎯⎯⎯⎯⎯⎯⎯⎯⎯⎯⎯⎯⎯⎯⎯⎯⎯⎯

⎯⎯⎯⎯⎯⎯⎯⎯⎯⎯⎯⎯⎯⎯⎯⎯⎯⎯⎯⎯⎯⎯⎯⎯⎯⎯⎯⎯⎯⎯⎯⎯⎯⎯

⎯⎯⎯⎯⎯⎯⎯⎯⎯⎯⎯⎯⎯⎯⎯⎯⎯⎯⎯⎯⎯⎯⎯⎯⎯⎯⎯⎯⎯⎯⎯⎯⎯⎯

⎯⎯⎯⎯⎯⎯⎯⎯⎯⎯⎯⎯⎯⎯⎯⎯⎯⎯⎯⎯⎯⎯⎯⎯⎯⎯⎯⎯⎯⎯⎯⎯⎯⎯

⎯⎯⎯⎯⎯⎯⎯⎯⎯⎯⎯⎯⎯⎯⎯⎯⎯⎯⎯⎯⎯⎯⎯⎯⎯⎯⎯⎯⎯⎯⎯⎯⎯⎯

⎯⎯⎯⎯⎯⎯⎯⎯⎯⎯⎯⎯⎯⎯⎯⎯⎯⎯⎯⎯⎯⎯⎯⎯⎯⎯⎯⎯⎯⎯⎯⎯⎯⎯

⎯⎯⎯⎯⎯⎯⎯⎯⎯⎯⎯⎯⎯⎯⎯⎯⎯⎯⎯⎯⎯⎯⎯⎯⎯⎯⎯⎯⎯⎯⎯⎯⎯⎯

Protein [　　] Fat [　　] Carbs [　　] Fiber [　　] Calories [　　]

Recipe: _____

Prep Time [   ] Cook Time [   ] Servings [   ] Difficulty [   ]

Ingredients

_____

_____

_____

_____

_____

_____

Directions

_____

_____

_____

_____

_____

_____

_____

_____

_____

_____

Protein [   ] Fat [   ] Carbs [   ] Fiber [   ] Calories [   ]

Recipe: ───────────────

Prep Time [   ] Cook Time [   ] Servings [   ] Difficulty [   ]

Ingredients

_____

_____

_____

_____

_____

_____

Directions

_____

_____

_____

_____

_____

_____

_____

_____

_____

Protein [   ] Fat [   ] Carbs [   ] Fiber [   ] Calories [   ]

Recipe: _____

Prep Time [   ] Cook Time [   ] Servings [   ] Difficulty [   ]

Ingredients

_____

_____

_____

_____

_____

_____

Directions

_____

_____

_____

_____

_____

_____

_____

_____

_____

_____

_____

Protein [   ] Fat [   ] Carbs [   ] Fiber [   ] Calories [   ]

Recipe: _____

Prep Time [   ] Cook Time [   ] Servings [   ] Difficulty [   ]

Ingredients

_____

_____

_____

_____

_____

_____

Directions

_____

_____

_____

_____

_____

_____

_____

_____

_____

_____

_____

Protein [   ] Fat [   ] Carbs [   ] Fiber [   ] Calories [   ]

22391003R00081

Printed in Great Britain
by Amazon